How to use this book

Say the sound.

Trace the letter shapes.

Point to the picture and say the word.

Blend to read the list of words.

ue ue ure

1

ue

rescue

cue
value
statue
muesli

-oo oo ar or ur ow oi

barbec**ue**

resc**ue**

ear air -er er -ue

What other words can you find in the picture with the /yoo/ sound in them?
[venue]

3

ue

glue

blue
clue
true
clueless

ar or ur ow oi ear air

tiss**ue**

-er er -ue -ue

What other words can you find in the picture with the long /oo/ sound in them?

[Sue]

ture  ure

pic**ture**

p**ure**

adventure
mixture
manure
manicure

ur ow oi ear air -er er

manic**ure**

pic**ture**

punc**ture**

-ue -ue -ture -ure

What other words can you find in the picture with the /yoor/ or /chu/ sound in them?

[man**ure**, crea**ture**]

 Trace the graphemes and say the sounds.

-ue oi ai oo -er air er oa

 Match the pictures to the graphemes.

9

Do not argue.

Is glue sticky?

Is it a blue vulture?

The nurse can cure you.

Hang the picture on the wall.

Let's have an adventure.

 Read the captions.

ow oi ai -ure ur air er

 Match the captions to the pictures. Which two captions do not have a picture?

Shh!

Look at this, Sue.

Watch the vulture,

So bright and blue.

It looks like a picture,

Or a small statue.

Read the poem. Sound out and blend any words that you do not know.